Practice Test for the Cognitive Abilities Test (CogAT®*) Level D

Practice Test 1

By Mercer Publishing

Practice Test for the

Cognitive Abilities Test (CogAT®*) Level D

Practice Test 1

A study aid to help your child get into a gifted program.

Mercer Publishing

* CogAT® is a registered trademark of the Houghton Mifflin Company which was not involved in the production of, and does not endorse, this practice test.

INTRODUCTION

As a parent and educator, I understand how important it is to ensure your children are given the opportunities they deserve when it comes to their education. One of the greatest opportunities your child will have is entering the gifted program, if they can qualify for the program based on their test scores.

One of the primary tools for measuring a student's ability to enter the gifted program is the Cognitive Abilities Test (CogAT®*) published by Riverside Publishing. This test is made up of tests in three areas: Verbal, Quantitative and Nonverbal. Your child's score on this test is likely the sole predictor of their inclusion, or non-inclusion, into the gifted program.

Most resources state that there are really no ways to prepare for this test - that your child should only get a good night's sleep before taking the test. An official practice test with sample questions does exist, but it is only available to licensed test administrators. It is guaranteed that if your child is not familiar with some of the symbols used in the test or if they have never done some of the types of problems before, that they will not do as well as they could on this test – perhaps jeopardizing their admission into the gifted program. So what should the average parent do?

If you have purchased this practice test, you have taken the first step. This practice test contains nine subtests in the three test areas found on the CogAT®* Multilevel Edition Level D exam, which is usually given to students in fifth grade**:

VERBAL

Verbal Classification	20 questions
Sentence Completion	20 questions
Verbal Analogies	25 questions

QUANTITATIVE

Quantitative Relations	25 questions
Number Series	20 questions
Equation Building	15 questions

NONVERBAL

Figure Classification	25 questions
Figure Analogies	25 questions
Figure Analysis	15 questions

The object of this practice test is to familiarize your child with the types of questions they will face on test day, how the tests are formatted, the symbols used and the number of questions in in each test area. However, since this practice test has not been standardized with Riverside Publishing and the actual CogAT®* exam, a valid CogAT®* test score cannot be concluded from their results on this practice test.

Good luck on this practice test and your upcoming gifted program exam.

Mercer Publishing

* CogAT® is a registered trademark of Houghton Mifflin Company, which was not involved in the production of, and does not endorse, this practice test.

** Based on the exam publisher's recommendation for testing gifted students. We cannot guarantee which level will be given by your school.

TABLE OF CONTENTS

TEST TAKING INFORMATION

The Cognitive Abilities Test (CogAT®*) Level D exam, which is usually given to students in fifth grade**, is a timed, multiple choice test. The test is self-administered, where the student reads and answers the questions themselves. Most testing for the CogAT®* Level D exam is done using electronically scored answer sheets, although answering in hand-scored booklets is sometimes also done.

The official guideline from the publisher is that students should not guess if they do not know the answer – that random guessing compromises the validity of the scores. However, the CogAT®* score is calculated based on the number of right answers and the student is not penalized for incorrect answers. As a parent looking for a high score, it is better for your child to answer all questions than leave an answer blank.

There are some approaches to standardized testing that have been proven to increase test scores. Review the following strategies with your child and have them practice these as they go through the practice test.

Listen Carefully. Instructions will be given to your child during the exam, including directions for each section and how to fill out the test forms. Many errors are made because children do not listen to the instructions as carefully as they should. If your child fills in the answers incorrectly or marks in the wrong section, your child's score will be lowered significantly.

Read the Entire Question. Some children begin filling in answers before they finish reading the entire question. It could be that the last part of the question has the information needed to answer the question correctly.

Look at all the Available Answers. In their desire to finish quickly or first, many children select the first answer that seems right to them without reading all of the answers and choosing the one that best answers the question. No additional points are given for finishing the test early. Make sure your child understands the importance of evaluating all the answers before choosing one.

Skip Difficult Questions – Return to Them Later. Many children will sit and worry about a hard question, spending so much time on one problem that they never get to problems that they would be able to answer correctly if they only had enough time. Explain to your child that they can always return to a difficult question once they finish the test section.

Eliminate Answer Choices. If your child can eliminate one or more of the answer choices as definitely wrong, their chances of guessing correctly among the remaining choices improve their odds of getting the answer right.

Practice Filling Out a Bubble Test Form. Many errors are made on the CogAT®* exam because the students do not know how to fill out a bubble test form. A sample test form has been included in Appendix A. Have your child practice filling in answers in the bubbles in the sample form so they will know what to expect on the exam day.

Now, on to the practice test.

---

* CogAT® is a registered trademark of Houghton Mifflin Company, which was not involved in the production of, and does not endorse, this practice test.

** Based on the exam publisher's recommendation for testing gifted students. We cannot guarantee which level will be given by your school.

VERBAL CLASSIFICATION

Each question in this section contains three words in bold letters. Review these words and determine why they are similar. Select the word from the five available answers that is most similar to the bold words.

20 questions
Approximate time to complete: 10 minutes

1. **ant   bee   butterfly**

   A. snake   B. ladybug   C. frog   D. insect   E. worm

2. **barn   tomato   ruby**

   A. farm   B. tractor   C. fire truck   D. basketball   E. lettuce

3. **year   minute   day**

   A. clock   B. calendar   C. second   D. date   E. time

4. **scissors   axe   knife**

   A. tool   B. hammer   C. saw   D. shovel   E. rope

5. **softball   lacrosse   skiing**

   a. competition   B. brave   C. win   D. contest   E. boxing

6. **whisk   grater   colander**

   A. spatula   B. brush   C. iron   D. wick   E. foil

7. **extra   additional   spare**

    A. surplus   B. simple   C. short   D. tall   E. meager

8. **crab   turtle   snail**

    A. fish   B. lizard   C. reptile   D. lobster   E. frog

9. **strike   out   ball**

    A. bat   B. foul   C. play   D. umpire   E. pitcher

10. **authority   control   rule**

    A. command   B. colonel   C. medal   D. fault   E. serge

11. **rabbit   squirrel   cat**

    A. goose   B. meow   C. mouse   D. fur   E. pet

12. **reimburse   restore   return**

    A. require   B. receive   C. produce   D. deserve   E. refund

13. **urban   municipal   city**

    a. metropolitan   B. efficient   C. elevated   D. rural   E. superior

14. **raft   tire   balloon**

   A. canoe   B. unicycle   C. beach ball D. wagon   E. truck

15. **underneath   below   under**

   A. above   B. beneath   C. bottom   D. next   E. strap

16. **she   him   he**

   A. her   B. we   C. us   D. them   E. they

17. **tomorrow   yesterday   always**

   A. year   B. season   C. calendar   D. never   E. further

18. **pride   school   flock**

   A. spirit   B. teacher   C. herd   D. allow   E. interest

19. **think   fall   run**

   A. tree   B. speed   C. ant   D. paper   E. orange

20. **hypothesis   assumption   speculation**

   A. perimeter   B. premise   C. fact   D. skill   E. knowledge

SENTENCE COMPLETION

Each sentence in this section is missing a word. Select the word from the five available answers that best completes the sentence.

20 questions
Approximate time to complete: 10 minutes

1.   Could you _____ the phone ring?

      A. feel   B. try   C. see   D. know   E. hear

2.   Would you like a_____ of chocolate cake?

      A. piece   B. platter   C. bar   D. whole   E. pie

3.   They are _____ of the nicest people I know.

      A. none   B. plenty   C. one   D. some   E. few

4.   _____ thank you, I don't want any.

      A. No   B. Yes   C. Who   D. Please   E. Show

5.   The golfer made a _____ in one.

      A. tee   B. hole   C. score   D. par   E. club

6.   She hurried to _____ the job she was offered.

      A. accept   B. save   C. blame   D. end   E. inhabit

7.	We bought some _____ at the lumber store.

	A. wood	B. tires	C. fabric	D. paper	E. cash

8.	They got the shovel to dig the _____.

	A. mound	B. hole	C. mud	D. pot	E. plant

9.	The bathroom is up the _____ and down the hall.

	A. building	B. stairs	C. hall	D. ladder	E. maze

10.	It is very nice to _____ you.

	A. learn	B. lose	C. meet	D. kick	E. forget

11.	We can't play without Jason, he's an _____ part of our team.

	A. integral	B. elite	C. intellectual	D. avid	E. integer

12.	I made a mistake, please _____ my previous instructions.

	A. disregard	B. expect	C. augment	D. disable	E. depict

13.	They couldn't drive past the _____.

	A. school	B. rehearsal	C. barricade	D. parade	E. park

14. A chameleon changes its skin color to hide from its _____.

    A. predators B. friends   C. dwelling D. food   E. vermin

15. Congress _____ the new law.

    A. elected B. ruled   C. directed D. taught E. enacted

16. She _____ her story to the whole class.

    A. read   B. blew   C. wrote   D. drew   E. gave

17. Our _____ car easily fits in the small parking spot.

    A. enormous B. deep   C. compact D. heavy   E. massive

18. I would love to see a real dinosaur if they weren't _____.

    A. distinct B. extinct   C. detached D. ravenous E. significant

19. The judge had to _____ the charges because there wasn't enough evidence.

    A. assign   B. order   C. dismiss D. forfeit   E. gavel

20. She was caught in a _____ between going out with her friends and finishing her homework.

    A. blizzard B. dilemma C. frenzy   D. diagram E. blunder

VERBAL ANALOGIES

Each question in this section contains three words in bold letters. Review the first two words and determine how they are related. Select the word from the five available answers that has the same relationship with the third word.

25 questions
Approximate time to complete: 10 minutes

1. **father ⟶ son : mother ⟶**

   A. aunt   B. girl   C. cousin   D. family   E. daughter

2. **inch ⟶ length : pound ⟶**

   A. hammer   B. wait   C. nail   D. volume   E. weight

3. **sugar ⟶ sweet : lemon ⟶**

   A. sour   B. yellow   C. sugary   D. wedge   E. honey

4. **fireman ⟶ ladder : farmer ⟶**

   A. farm   B. cow   C. tractor   D. barn   E. hay

5. **urban ⟶ metropolitan : country ⟶**

   A. rural   B. state   C. continent   D. town   E. municipal

6. **notice ⟶ ignore : alone ⟶**

   A. lonely   B. isolated   C. together   D. beside   E. disregard

7.   pages ⟶ book : banana ⟶

   A. tree   B. bunch   C. group   D. monkey   E. fruit

8.   bring ⟶ brought : try ⟶

   A. attempt   B. test   C. taste   D. experiment E. tried

9.   shout ⟶ exclaim : substitute ⟶

   A. teacher   B. contribute C. record   D. replace   E. remove

10. good ⟶ splendid : bad ⟶

   A. disobedient B. inadequate C. wicked   D. miserly   E. injure

11. word ⟶ letter : music ⟶

   A. guitar   B. sheet   C. note   D. instrument E. band

12. first ⟶ second : second ⟶

   A. first   B. second   C. third   D. place   E. order

13. hill ⟶ mountain : lake ⟶

   A. pond   B. water   C. river   D. ocean   E. fish

14. camel ⟶ dromedary : chicken ⟶

    A. coop   B. farm   C. rooster   D. hen   E. fowl

15. assess ⟶ evaluate : abbreviate ⟶

    A. increase   B. prolong   C. shorten   D. ponder   E. reflect

16. fish ⟶ chips : milk ⟶

    A. cow   B. gallon   C. cookies   D. cream   E. cheese

17. gather ⟶ collect : distribute ⟶

    A. lose   B. take   C. share   D. give   E. leave

18. several ⟶ numerous : seldom ⟶

    A. often   B. least   C. never   D. miniscule   E. maximum

19. start ⟶ revive : create ⟶

    A. make   B. destroy   C. design   D. reproduce   E. imagine

20. thermometer ⟶ temperature : odometer ⟶

    A. time   B. heat   C. weight   D. distance   E. measure

21. crowded ⟶ sparse : giant ⟶

    A. thick   B. tall   C. intense   D. obscure   E. miniature

22. chick ⟶ rooster : offspring ⟶

    A. infant   B. grow   C. parent   D. season   E. coil

23. knife ⟶ fork : ball ⟶

    A. game   B. sport   C. sphere   D. bounce   E. chain

24. stop ⟶ halt : hinder ⟶

    A. discontinue B. ban   C. establish   D. onset   E. impede

25. excursion ⟶ expedition : falter ⟶

    A. persist   B. mistake   C. hesitate   D. flaw   E. blame

QUANTITATIVE RELATIONS

Each question in this section contains two items to compare. Review items I and II. Determine if one is greater than the other or if they are equal. Then select the answer that reflects that relationship.

25 questions
Approximate time to complete: 12 minutes

1. I. 3 + 3 + 3 + 3
    II. 4 + 4 + 4

    A. I is greater than II.
    B. I is less than II.
    C. I is equal to II.

2. I. 30 percent
    II. 55 percent

    A. I is greater than II.
    B. I is less than II.
    C. I is equal to II.

3. I. hexagon
    II. pentagon

    A. I has more sides than II.
    B. I has fewer sides than II.
    C. I has the same number of sides as II.

4. I. 52 + 66
    II. 44 + 91

    A. I is greater than II.
    B. I is less than II.
    C. I is equal to II.

5. I. 19 cents
    II. 1 dime + 1 nickel + 4 pennies

    A. I is greater than II.
    B. I is less than II.
    C. I is equal to II.

6. I. 60 degrees
    II. 180 degrees

    A. I is greater than II.
    B. I is less than II.
    C. I is equal to II.

7.　　I. 12 x 12　　　　　　　　A. I is greater than II.
　　　II. 11 x 13　　　　　　　　B. I is less than II.
　　　　　　　　　　　　　　　　C. I is equal to II.

8.　　I. 39821　　　　　　　　　A. I is greater than II.
　　　II. 39817　　　　　　　　　B. I is less than II.
　　　　　　　　　　　　　　　　C. I is equal to II.

9.　　I. 199 – 50　　　　　　　　A. I is greater than II.
　　　II. 99 + 50　　　　　　　　B. I is less than II.
　　　　　　　　　　　　　　　　C. I is equal to II.

10.　 I. 3.33　　　　　　　　　　A. I is greater than II.
　　　II. 3.333　　　　　　　　　B. I is less than II.
　　　　　　　　　　　　　　　　C. I is equal to II.

11.　 I. 50 nickels　　　　　　　A. I is greater than II.
　　　II. 2 dollars　　　　　　　B. I is less than II.
　　　　　　　　　　　　　　　　C. I is equal to II.

12.　 I. 400 – 179　　　　　　　A. I is greater than II.
　　　II. 179　　　　　　　　　　B. I is less than II.
　　　　　　　　　　　　　　　　C. I is equal to II.

13.　 I. 39874　　　　　　　　　A. I is greater than II.
　　　II. 39905　　　　　　　　　B. I is less than II.
　　　　　　　　　　　　　　　　C. I is equal to II.

14. I. 24 inches
     II. 2 feet

A. I is longer than II.
B. I is shorter than II.
C. I is the same length as II.

15. I. 1.2
     II. 1.3

A. I is greater than II.
B. I is less than II.
C. I is equal to II.

16. I. parallelogram
     II. hexagon

A. I has more sides than II.
B. I has fewer sides than II.
C. I has the same number of sides as II.

17. I. 40030
     II. 40062

A. I is greater than II.
B. I is less than II.
C. I is equal to II.

18. I. 918 + 18
     II. 981 – 51

A. I is greater than II.
B. I is less than II.
C. I is equal to II.

19. I. 3 boys
     II. 1 girl and a cat

A. I has more legs than II.
B. I has fewer legs than II.
C. I has the same number of legs as II.

20. I. 2 inches
     II. 1/4 foot

A. I is longer than II.
B. I is shorter than II.
C. I is the same length as II.

21.   I. $1010 + 110 + 10$ A. I is greater than II.
       II. $1020 + 102 + 10$ B. I is less than II.
                                        C. I is equal to II.

22.   I. 39848   A. I is greater than II.
       II. 39852   B. I is less than II.
                                        C. I is equal to II.

23.   I. $40.4 + 10$ A. I is greater than II.
       II. 50.4   B. I is less than II.
                                        C. I is equal to II.

24.   I. -2   A. I is greater than II.
       II. -1   B. I is less than II.
                                      C. I is equal to II.

25.   I. $852 - 25$ A. I is greater than II.
       II. $825 - 52$ B. I is less than II.
                                      C. I is equal to II.

NUMBER SERIES

Each question in this section contains a series of numbers in bold. Review the numbers to determine the rule for their order. Select the number from the five available answers that should come next in the series.

20 questions
Approximate time to complete: 12 minutes

1.   **15 20 25 30 35** ⟶

  A. 35   B. 45   C. 55   D. 40   E. 50

2.   **300 250 200 150 100** ⟶

  A. 0   B. 50   C. 100   D. 90   E. 70

3.   **6 9 3 6 9** ⟶

  A. 9   B. 10   C. 1   D. 3   E. 5

4.   **64 57 50 43 36** ⟶

  A. 35   B. 29   C. 32   D. 30   E. 27

5.   **1 2 4 5 7** ⟶

  A. 10   B. 9   C. 8   D. 7   E. 6

6.   **9 3 9 3 9** ⟶

  A. 9   B. 10   C. 1   D. 3   E. 5

7. **5 5 6 6 7** ⟶

   A. 7   B. 9   C. 4   D. 10   E. 8

8. **71 87 103 119 135** ⟶

   A. 149   B. 151   C. 155   D. 148   E. 150

9. **32 22 14 8 4** ⟶

   A. 1   B. 2   C. 3   D. 4   E. 0

10. **84 71 58 45 32** ⟶

   A. 19   B. 30   C. 29   D. 15   E. 18

11. **27 29 33 39 47** ⟶

   A. 57   B. 51   C. 56   D. 51   E. 55

12. **8.25 9.5 10.75 12 13.25** ⟶

   A. 15   B. 14.25   C. 14.75   D. 14.5   E. 14

13. **72 113 154 195 236** ⟶

   A. 277   B. 287   C. 299   D. 249.   E. 251

14. **8 9 10 12 14 17** ⟶

    A. 22   B. 19   C. 21   D. 20   E. 18

15. **6.5 9 11.5 14 16.5** ⟶

    A. 17   B. 18.5   C. 18   D. 19.5   E. 19

16. **3 1 4 2 5** ⟶

    A. 6   B. 3   C. 2   D. 7   E. 5

17. **0 0 7 0 0** ⟶

    A. 6   B. 2   C. 7   D. 9   E. 0

18. **2 0 3 1 4** ⟶

    A. 2   B. 4   C. 3   D. 5   E. 1

19. **113 108 103 98 93** ⟶

    A. 92   B. 91   C. 90   D. 89   E. 88

20. **14 15 18 23 30** ⟶

    A. 36   B. 40   C. 41   D. 37   E. 39

EQUATION BUILDING

Each question in this section contains a series of numbers and numerical signs in bold. Arrange and rearrange each of the numbers and signs to come up with one of the five available answers.

15 questions
Approximate time to complete: 16 minutes

1. **9 10 10 + +**

    A. 27   B. 9   C. 26   D. 28   E. 29

2. **1 2 1 x +**

    A. 3   B. 0   C. 2   D. 6   E. 1

3. **1 1 10 + -**

    A. 1   B. 5   C. 0   D. 15   E. 10

4. **1 2 7 x -**

    A. 15   B. 13   C. 1   D. 0   E. 10

5. **3 10 3 - -**

    A. 3   B. 6   C. 4   D. 0   E. 9

6. **3 6 5 x +**

    A. 3   B. 18   C. 22   D. 28   E. 23

7. **3   5   5   x   -**

   A. 27   B. 3   C. 0   D. 8   E. 22

8. **6   8   10   x   -**

   A. 43   B. 6   C. 0   D. 8   E. 38

9. **4   2   8   +   -**

   A. 8   B. 0   C. 6   D. 4   E. 7

10. **10   9   10   x   x**

   A. 90   B. 890   C. 9000   D. 910   E. 900

11. **7   7   4   x   -**

   A. 26   B. 7   C. 20   D. 21   E. 0

12. **8   4   1   -   -**

   A. 3   B. 6   C. 0   D. 8   E. 9

13. **6   4   8   x   +**

   A. 39   B. 6   C. 38   D. 34   E. 80

14.   **5**   **8**   **10**   **x**   **-**

     A. 39   B. 47   C. 0   D. 5   E. 42

15.   **9**   **10**   **4**   **+**   **-**

     A. 9   B. 2   C. 4   D. 5   E. 0

FIGURE CLASSIFICATION

Review the first three figures in each question and determine why they are similar. Select the figure from the five available answers that is most similar to the first three figures.

25 questions
Approximate time to complete: 10 minutes

1.

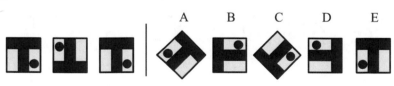

2.

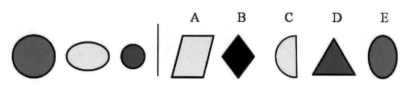

3.

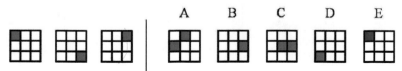

4.

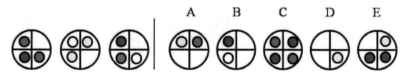

5.

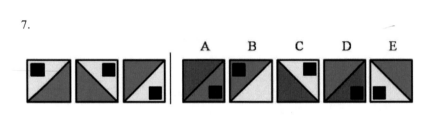

6.

7.

8.

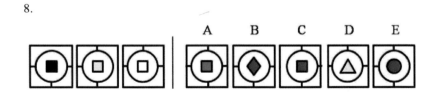

9.

10.

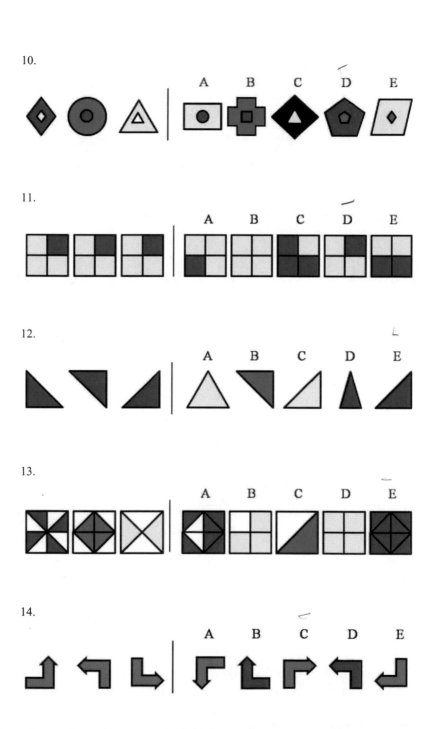

11.

12.

13.

14.

15.

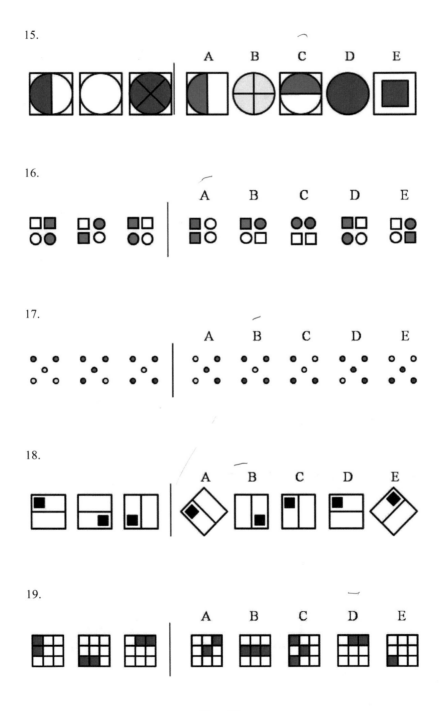

16.

17.

18.

19.

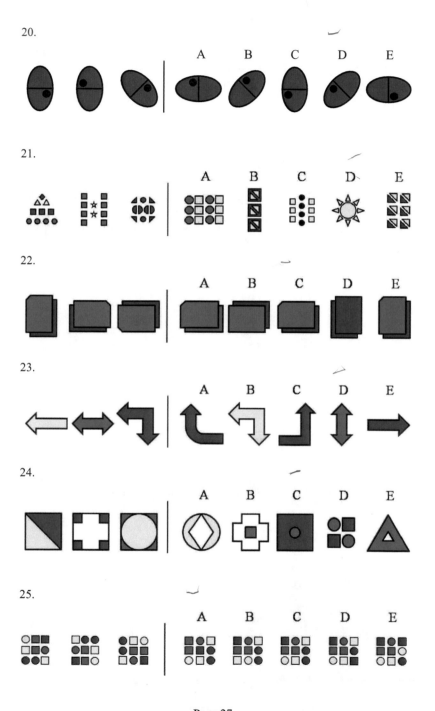

20.

21.

22.

23.

24.

25.

FIGURE ANALOGIES

Review the first two figures in each question. The first figure is modified into the second figure in some way. Select the figure from the five available answers that will be created when that same modification is done to the third figure.

25 questions
Approximate time to complete: 10 minutes

1.

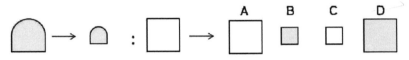

2.

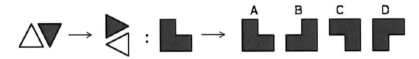

3.

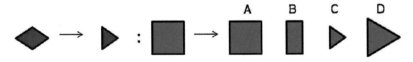

4.

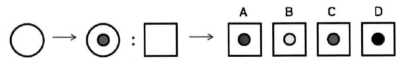

5.

6.

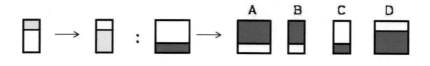

7.

8.

9.

Page 29

© 2010 Mercer Publishing

10.

11.

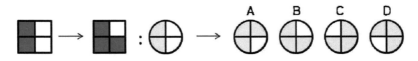

12.

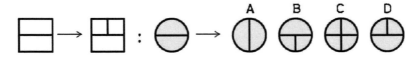

13.

14.

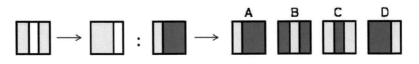

15.

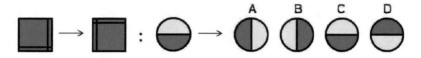

16.

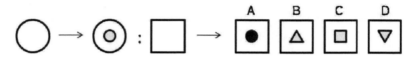

17.

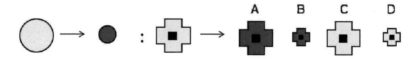

18.

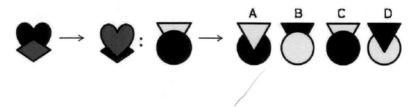

19.

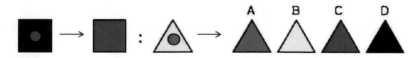

20.

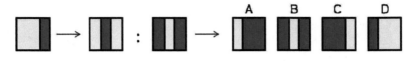

21.

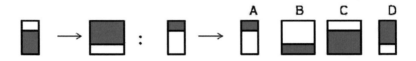

22.

23.

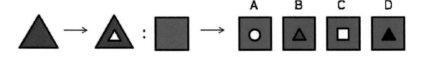

24.

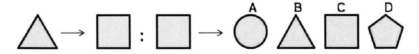

25.

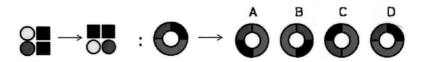

FIGURE ANALYSIS

Each question in this section shows a square piece of paper being folded and then hole-punched. Select the piece of paper from the five available answers that shows how the paper will look when it is unfolded.

15 questions
Approximate time to complete: 10 minutes

1.

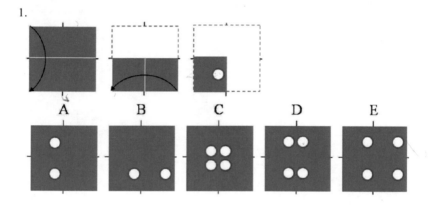

2.

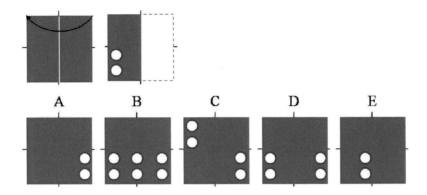

3.

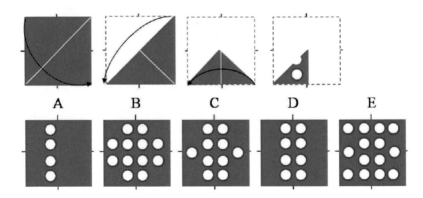

4.

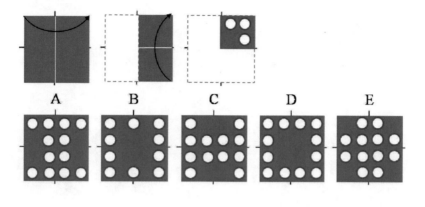

5.

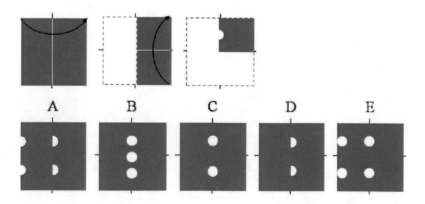

6.

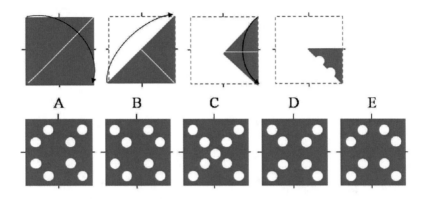

7.

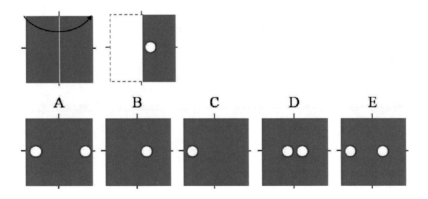

8.

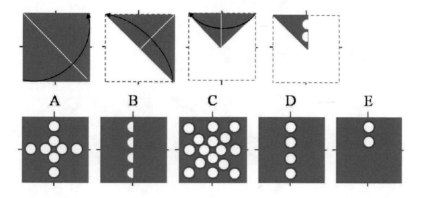

9.

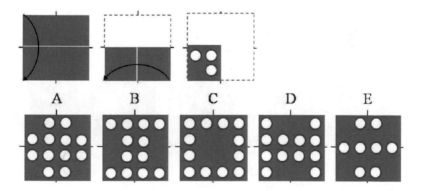

10.

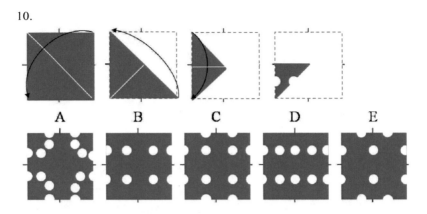

11.

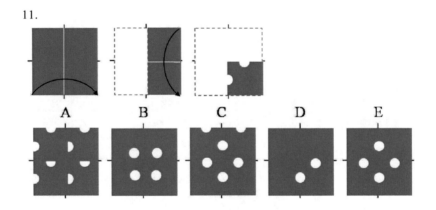

12.

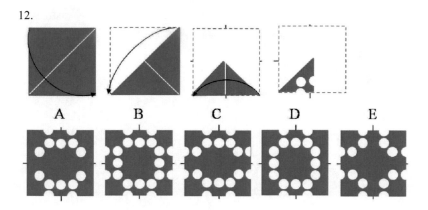

13.

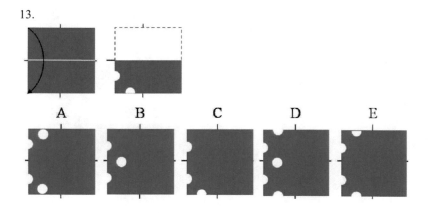

14.

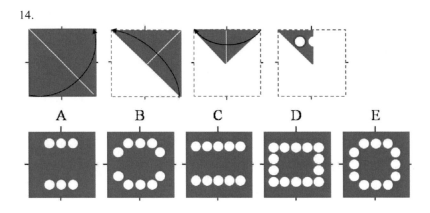

15.

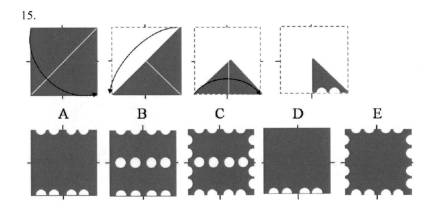

ANSWERS

VERBAL CLASSIFICATION

1. B. Insects
2. C. Things that are Red
3. C. Time Measurements
4. C. Things that Cut
5. E. Sports
6. A. Kitchen Utensils
7. A. Synonyms
8. D. Things with Shells
9. B. Calls an Umpire Makes
10. A. Synonyms
11. C. Mammals
12. E. Synonyms
13. A. Synonyms
14. C. Things that are Inflated
15. B. Prepositions Related to Below
16. A. Pronouns for one person
17. D. Words Describing Days
18. C. Types of Animal Group Names
19. B. Verbs
20. B. Synonyms

SENTENCE COMPLETION

1. E. hear
2. A. piece
3. D. some
4. A. No
5. B. hole
6. A. accept
7. A. wood
8. B. hole
9. B. stairs
10. C. meet
11. A. integral
12. A. disregard
13. C. barricade
14. A. predators
15. E. enacted
16. A. read
17. C. compact
18. B. extinct
19. C. dismiss
20. B. dilemma

VERBAL ANALOGIES

1. E. Similar Relationship
2. E. A Type or Example of.
3. A. Object and Its Property (i.e. Color)
4. C. Performer and the object
5. A. Similar
6. C. Opposite
7. B. Object that is part of the whole
8. E. Similar (Past Tense)
9. D. Similar
10. C. Degree
11. C. Groups or Part of the Group
12. C. Similar Placement
13. D. Degrees
14. E. A Type or Example of.
15. C. Similar
16. C. Things that go together
17. D. Similar
18. C. Degrees
19. D. Similar (Done Again)
20. D. Object and how/where it is used
21. E. Opposite
22. C. Younger or Older Version
23. E. Things that go together
24. E. Similar
25. C. Similar

QUANTITATIVE RELATIONS

1. C
2. B
3. A
4. B
5. C
6. B
7. A
8. A
9. C
10. B
11. A
12. A
13. B
14. C
15. B
16. B
17. B
18. A
19. C
20. B
21. B
22. B
23. C
24. B
25. A

NUMBER SERIES

1. D. Add 5 each time
2. B. Subtract 50 each time
3. D. The first three numbers are repeated.
4. B. Subtract 7 each time
5. C. Add 1, 2, 1, 2, 1
6. D. The first two numbers are repeated.
7. A. Add 1 to the first number to get the third number. Add 1 to
   the second number to get the fourth.
8. B. Add 16 each time
9. B. Subtract 10, 8, 6, 4, 2
10. A. Subtract 13 each time
11. A. Add 2, 4, 6, 8, 10
12. D. Add 1.25 each time
13. A. Add 41 each time
14. D. Add 1, 1, 2, 2, 3, 3
15. E. Add 2.5 each time
16. B. Add 1 to the first number to get the third number. Add 1 to
   the second number to get the fourth.
17. C. The first three numbers are repeated.
18. A. Add 1 to the first number to get the third number. Add 1 to
   the second number to get the fourth.
19. E. Subtract 5 each time
20. E. Add 1, 3, 5, 7, 9

EQUATION BUILDING

1. E. 9 + 10 + 10 = 29
2. A. 1 x 2 + 1 = 3
3. E. 1 + 10 - 1 = 10
4. B. 2 x 7 - 1 = 13
5. C. 10 - 3 - 3 = 4
6. E. 3 x 6 + 5 = 23
7. E. 5 x 5 - 3 = 22
8. E. 6 x 8 - 10 = 38
9. C. 2 + 8 - 4 = 6
10. E. 10 x 9 x 10 = 900
11. D. 7 x 4 - 7 = 21
12. A. 8 - 4 - 1 = 3
13. C. 4 x 8 + 6 = 38
14. E. 5 x 10 - 8 = 42
15. D. 10 + 4 - 9 = 5

FIGURE CLASSIFICATION

1. E. Each figure is rounded (circle or oval).
2. E. Each figure has three inner circles.
3. B. Each figure is the same, only rotated. The black dot should be in the same location.
4. D. Each figure has one blue corner square
5. D. Each figure is a white pentagon.
6. C. Each figure has no rounded sides.
7. E. Each figure is blue and yellow and has a black square in the yellow half.
8. C. Each figure has an inner square and three lines between the circle and square
9. E. Each figure has 4 circles.
10. D. Each figure has the same inner and outer shape
11. D. Each figure has 1 red and 3 yellow quadrants (in the same position).
12. E. Each figure is red and a rotation of the same triangle
13. C. Each figure is half-shaded.
14. A. Each figure is the same only rotated. The arrow in the wrong answers is backwards.
15. C. Each figure has a square and a circle
16. D. Each figure has two side-by-side squares and two side-by-side circles. One circle and one square is blue.
17. D. Each figure has the top two dots blue
18. D. Each figure is the same, only rotated. The black square should be in the same location.
19. D. Each figure has two red squares, but not the center square
20. B. Each figure is the same, only rotated. The black dot should be in the same location.
21. C. Each figure has 10 shapes.
22. E. Each figure is a rotation of the same figure
23. B. Each figure is an arrow that points left.
24. C. Each figure has an outer square.
25. C. Each figure is a rotation of the same figure

FIGURE ANALOGIES

1. C. Reduce Size of Figure.
2. B. Rotate Counterclockwise.
3. B. Whole to Half Shape.
4. C. Add Blue Dot.
5. B. Flip Vertically.
6. A. Reverse Colors.
7. B. Remove 1 Line.
8. A. Rotate 180 Degrees, Color Change.
9. A. Enlarge Width.
10. D. Whole to Half Shape (Left Half).
11. B. Color Bottom Right Quarter.
12. D. Add 1/2 Line to Top Half.
13. D. Flip Vertically.
14. B. Move Bar 1/3 Right.
15. D. Rotate 180 Degrees.
16. C. Add Yellow Inner Shape (Same Shape as Outer Shape).
17. B. Reduce Size of Figure, Color Change.
18. D. Reverse the Order, Reverse Colors.
19. A. Same Shape, Color Change to Dot Color, Remove Dot.
20 A. Move Bar 1/3 Left.
21. B. Enlarge Width, Flip Vertically.
22 D. Color Bottom Right Quarter.
23. C. Add White Inner Shape (Same Shape as Outer Shape).
24. D. Add 1 Side.
25. C. Rotate Counterclockwise.

FIGURE ANALYSIS

1. D
2. D
3. B
4. D
5. C
6. D
7. D
8. A
9. A
10. C
11. E
12. B
13. E
14. E
15. E

BUBBLE TEST FORM

Many errors are made on the CogAT®* exam because the students do not know how to fill out a bubble test form. Have your child practice filling in answers in the bubbles below.

1	Ⓐ Ⓑ Ⓒ Ⓓ Ⓔ					1	Ⓐ Ⓑ Ⓒ Ⓓ Ⓔ		
2	Ⓐ Ⓑ Ⓒ Ⓓ Ⓔ					2	Ⓐ Ⓑ Ⓒ Ⓓ Ⓔ		
3	Ⓐ Ⓑ Ⓒ Ⓓ Ⓔ					3	Ⓐ Ⓑ Ⓒ Ⓓ Ⓔ		
4	Ⓐ Ⓑ Ⓒ Ⓓ Ⓔ					4	Ⓐ Ⓑ Ⓒ Ⓓ Ⓔ		
5	Ⓐ Ⓑ Ⓒ Ⓓ Ⓔ					5	Ⓐ Ⓑ Ⓒ Ⓓ Ⓔ		
6	Ⓐ Ⓑ Ⓒ Ⓓ Ⓔ					6	Ⓐ Ⓑ Ⓒ Ⓓ Ⓔ		
7	Ⓐ Ⓑ Ⓒ Ⓓ Ⓔ					7	Ⓐ Ⓑ Ⓒ Ⓓ Ⓔ		
8	Ⓐ Ⓑ Ⓒ Ⓓ Ⓔ					8	Ⓐ Ⓑ Ⓒ Ⓓ Ⓔ		
9	Ⓐ Ⓑ Ⓒ Ⓓ Ⓔ					9	Ⓐ Ⓑ Ⓒ Ⓓ Ⓔ		
10	Ⓐ Ⓑ Ⓒ Ⓓ Ⓔ					10	Ⓐ Ⓑ Ⓒ Ⓓ Ⓔ		
11	Ⓐ Ⓑ Ⓒ Ⓓ Ⓔ					11	Ⓐ Ⓑ Ⓒ Ⓓ Ⓔ		
12	Ⓐ Ⓑ Ⓒ Ⓓ Ⓔ					12	Ⓐ Ⓑ Ⓒ Ⓓ Ⓔ		
13	Ⓐ Ⓑ Ⓒ Ⓓ Ⓔ					13	Ⓐ Ⓑ Ⓒ Ⓓ Ⓔ		
14	Ⓐ Ⓑ Ⓒ Ⓓ Ⓔ					14	Ⓐ Ⓑ Ⓒ Ⓓ Ⓔ		
15	Ⓐ Ⓑ Ⓒ Ⓓ Ⓔ					15	Ⓐ Ⓑ Ⓒ Ⓓ Ⓔ		
16	Ⓐ Ⓑ Ⓒ Ⓓ Ⓔ					16	Ⓐ Ⓑ Ⓒ Ⓓ Ⓔ		
17	Ⓐ Ⓑ Ⓒ Ⓓ Ⓔ					17	Ⓐ Ⓑ Ⓒ Ⓓ Ⓔ		
18	Ⓐ Ⓑ Ⓒ Ⓓ Ⓔ					18	Ⓐ Ⓑ Ⓒ Ⓓ Ⓔ		
19	Ⓐ Ⓑ Ⓒ Ⓓ Ⓔ					19	Ⓐ Ⓑ Ⓒ Ⓓ Ⓔ		
20	Ⓐ Ⓑ Ⓒ Ⓓ Ⓔ					20	Ⓐ Ⓑ Ⓒ Ⓓ Ⓔ		
21	Ⓐ Ⓑ Ⓒ Ⓓ Ⓔ					21	Ⓐ Ⓑ Ⓒ Ⓓ Ⓔ		
22	Ⓐ Ⓑ Ⓒ Ⓓ Ⓔ					22	Ⓐ Ⓑ Ⓒ Ⓓ Ⓔ		
23	Ⓐ Ⓑ Ⓒ Ⓓ Ⓔ					23	Ⓐ Ⓑ Ⓒ Ⓓ Ⓔ		
24	Ⓐ Ⓑ Ⓒ Ⓓ Ⓔ					24	Ⓐ Ⓑ Ⓒ Ⓓ Ⓔ		
25	Ⓐ Ⓑ Ⓒ Ⓓ Ⓔ					25	Ⓐ Ⓑ Ⓒ Ⓓ Ⓔ		

MERCER PUBLISHING

Mercer Publishing understands how important it is to ensure your children are given the opportunities they deserve when it comes to their education. One of the greatest opportunities your child will have is entering the gifted program, if they can qualify for the program based on their test scores.

We provide practice test books for gifted program entry exams that offer:

- Similar questions and test formats to the actual tests
- Full-length practice tests
- Answer keys

These books are invaluable tools for your child to score their best - and get into the gifted program!

Please visit our website to find out the current gifted program exams that are available.

WWW.MERCERPUBLISHING.COM